# SULAMITH WÜLFING
## *Nature Spirits*

# SULAMITH WÜLFING

*Nature Spirits*

**Bluestar Communications** ®
Orinda, California

© 2002 Bluestar Communications, Orinda, California

Published by:
Bluestar Communications
162 Camino Don Miguel
Orinda, CA 94563
Tel: 800-6-Bluestar

Edited in part by Ann West
Cover Art by Sulamith Wülfing
Cover Design & Layout: Annette Wagner

**Text:**

*Elementals* by Flower A. Newhouse, © *Christward Ministry, Escondido, California*
Excerpt from: Flower A. Newhouse, *Angels of Nature*, Escondido 2002

*Lapis Lazuli or Why the Dwarfs Are Invisible, The Little Fairy* by Peter Michel, © *Aquamarin Verlag, Grafing, Germany*
Excerpts from: Peter Michel, *The Enchanted Aquamarine*, Grafing, Germany 1985

*Angels of Nature* by Flower A. Newhouse, © *Christward Ministry, Escondido, California*
Excerpts from: Flower A. Newhouse, *Angels of Nature*, Escondido 2002

*Fairies* and *Tree Spirits* by Dora van Gelder-Kunz, © *The Theosophical Publishing House, Wheaton, Illinois*
Excerpts from: Dora van Gelder, *The Real World of Fairies*. Copyright © 1977, 1999. Reprinted by permission of Quest Books/The Theosophical Publishing House, Wheaton, Illinois.

*The Little Man, The Cherry Tree, Fairy Dance, Helpful Dwarfs* by Marjorie Johnson, © *Aquamarin Verlag, Garfing, Germany*
Excerpts from: Marjorie Johnson, *Nature Spirits*, Aquamarin, Grafing, Germany 2000

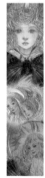

**All Illustrations:**
© 2002 Bluestar Communications, Orinda, California

First printing 2002
ISBN: 1-885394-57-8

Printed in Germany

# CONTENTS

# ELEMENTALS

The earth we walk is home to countless elementals. They serve the God force ruling all of nature obediently and without opposition. They cannot comprehend why we humans do not do likewise. Elementals never know weariness, and laziness is absolutely foreign to their experience. Their own advancement in angelic evolution takes place as their enthusiasm ripens and expands, thus increasing their size. The time comes when something akin to intelligence begins to function. At this point they are at the threshold of the stages of devahood.

More stories are told about elementals than about the angelic inhabitants of the other natural realms. Elementals appear in fairy tales and have given rise to a wealth of folklore, Irish mythology in particular is rich in tales of the little people, and more recently J.R.R. Tolkien's stories about Bilbo, the Hobbit, and the Middle Earth continue this tradition. For their part, elementals see into the motivation of humans, and they often do not like what

7

they see. They are particularly distraught when they encounter a reservoir of destructive human thought or a pile of human-made refuse. Elementals will work to rid the earth of these aberrations, but so consequential is the fallout from misguided human emotions and motives that hurricanes, earthquakes, and all manner of so-called natural disasters often result.

Earth elementals, in particular, are normally charming and precious to behold. The exceptions occur when they have cause to worry about someone's selfishness or the suffering of an animal. Then every part of the affected elemental looks worried and wrinkled. This expression is short-lived, however, as the Angels in charge of these delightful beings remind them to release these feelings at once, as they serve no constructive purpose. They are then encouraged to generate some impetus or impulse for the good that might offset the source of selfishness or suffering.

Earth Elementals are as common as the grasses and flowers. They are a teeming population of living beings, who take no particular notice of humans as they tirelessly go about their endeavors. These delightfully busy creatures create a sea

of luminescent activity across the landscape. Their appearance varies with the locale, but they have in common a light-filled essence that is reminiscent of butterflies fluttering among a field of flowers. Their exquisite little faces radiate a joyous quality. Their hands and feet are also visible, while the rest of what would constitute their bodies often dissolves in soft glowing clusters of light.

The one quality earth elementals expect of humans is unselfishness. Selfishness is beyond their comprehension, and they are strongly repelled by it. One of the most important traits for humans to cultivate in order to harmonize with elementals is generosity. When people are open-hearted and naturally good, tiny elementals actually enter their homes, which is quite a compliment to the human's character.

Elementals contribute to the atmosphere and ambience of the places we live in. When we leave homes and travel to a distant region where elementals are of a different constitution, we often experience a form of homesickness. For instance, when Flower A. Newhouse was traveling in the Pacific Northwest some years ago, she felt a particular longing for southern California and its habitat. Since she

was surrounded by exquisite scenery at the time, this feeling puzzled her, and she was prompted to ask her Guardian Angel what was behind her reaction. The Guardian Angel answered that she missed the energy of the elementals native to the southwest and to Mexico who worked with more ardor and enthusiasm. The elementals of the northwest and eastern United States, she was told, are more passive.

A vast company of elementals also serves throughout the mineral kingdom. What is noteworthy about these industrious beings is the brightness of the area around their hearts, which signifies the wealth of feeling they invest in their selfless labors. Mineral elementals are childlike in body, although their faces are not always youthful. Their work is to nourish and refine the qualities that make each mineral distinctive. They tend to specialize, concentrating on particular minerals such as copper, iron, gold, or silver. Of special interest are those beings associated with precious gemstones which are the culmination of a mineral's perfection, equivalent to redwoods and sequoias in the plant world. However, these devoted servers give the same level of care to all minerals, regardless of their value by worldly standards.

13

Elementals make their final appearance in the form of *frakins*, more commonly called *fairies*. Varying in height from eight to twelve inches, frakins are beautiful creatures possessing a child-like appearance that reflects either their feminine of masculine qualities. Frakins, like all the beings who wear etheric bodies, experience birth and death. Unlike humans, they are not born of mothers. They are fashioned by higher intelligences who created them from elemental essence. They exist in the etheric plane of earth for approximately a century and share responsibility for the flowering plants, grasses, and other smaller forms of vegetable life.

The work of frakins is energizing etherically the simplest cells of life through regular rhythmic breathing, a practice which recharges the earth's surface to a depth of three feet. Etheric breathing, rather than use of the hands, is the customary means by which frakins and other elementals impress, quicken, and energize the plant life in their care.

14

Flower spent many happy moments observing the work of these delightful creatures. On one occasion, she tells us, "as I walked from my chapel study to our home, I paused at the sight of nearly a hundred elemental creatures flying slowly from flower to flower. Before me was a cover of blue-eyed grass mixed with owl's clover, Indian paint brush, monkey flower and blossoming chemise. There was a delicate lyrical hum over the heads of the blue-eyed grass. I stood enraptured by the loveliness of these busy visitors."

Ranked above the frakins are the *elves*. Elves are somewhat larger than frakins, ranging from fifteen to twenty-four inches in height. They are also more vigorous and more clearly defined in form. As with all small angelic creatures, their size increases and decreases as a function of the contraction and expansion of their breathing, a process that is slower and deeper in the world of nature angels than in that of humans. Elves are entrusted with the care of larger plants and shrubs, those which attain a

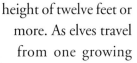

height of twelve feet or more. As elves travel from one growing

form in their domain to another, each plant receives a surcharging of the energies circulating through its etheric body; its life is thus maintained and strengthened.

*Gnomes* are more evolved than elves, and they are larger still. In children's legends and folklore, beings of this general group are occasionally called *brownies*. Unlike the fanciful image that many people have, such as gnomes wearing quaint human clothing, gnomes prefer to be attired in what appears to be leaves and flowers. They are very responsive to thoughtful direction and are more advances than the most intelligent domestic animals. They typically live for as long as three centuries. Among themselves, gnomes have names and experience ecstasies, fears, and disappointments comparable to those of humans.

To win acceptance and recognition from the angels of nature, we must approach them with genuine interest in their particular fields of service. When an individual evidences a love for the soil and growing life, its sculptured rocks, majestic mountains, and green forests, such a person comes under the watchful care of nature's angelic guardians. Should one of the gnomes take an interest in a

human being, the gnome might disclose one of the particular treasures under his of her care. The treasure might be a simple keepsake or a rich mineral deposit of considerable worth.

Flower has often experienced while walking in the wilderness, of finding symbolic "treasures"—a beautifully formed piece of wood, a stone, or a piece of bark. Often her attention was drawn to these objects by a gnome or other nature being. Each find would have a special significance. For instance, a piece of wood with a knothole might be a symbol of the third eye clairvoyance or of seeing an emotional situation clearly, depending on one's consciousness at the time. One time, she brought home a rather large piece of wood, which so clearly resembled a unicorn's head that everyone who saw it assumed that it had been carved by a human artist.

On the other hand, whenever humans poison the etheric energies of nature through pollution or selfish habits, serious karmic consequences result. If out of greed, for example, what was formally a cherished natural shrine becomes wasteland, there will be serious repercussions. Those who deal violently with nature are often killed

19

violently by nature. But those who have the wisdom and thankfulness of spirit to enter nature with reverence find a heartwarming return of respect and loyalty.

Excerpt from: Flower A. Newhouse, *Angels of Nature*, Escondido 2002

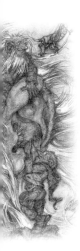

## LAPIS LAZULI
## OR
## WHY THE DWARFS ARE INVISIBLE

In olden times, when dwarfs still lived in harmony with humans, a wise king named Lapis Lazuli ruled the land of the dwarfs. His palace was on a large mountain that was covered by a verdant forest of fir. The humans called this mountain Dark Forest.

There were far fewer dwarfs than humans, but the dwarfs were tough and industrious. Almost all of them worked below the surface of the earth, where they mined coal ore and silver, among other things. They sold these useful metals to the humans in exchange for food. This kind of trade existed for centuries with hardly ever a quarrel as a result.

The dwarfs not only mined ordinary goods for daily life, but they also had the special honor of managing the gemstone mines. No one but the dwarfs was allowed to know the location of the different types of mines. Therefore, each king would pass on this knowledge to his successor just briefly before his own death.

It worked like this. The dwarfs never fell sick, for they knew about the laws of nature and never broke those laws. As a result, they knew when the life of the king was about to end, which let them safely pass on the knowledge about the mines from one ruler to the next.

However, not only did the location of the mines need to be preserved, but also the understanding of the mysterious powers held by the various gemstones.

At the coronation of each king, he would choose a gemstone as his throne name—the jewel he considered most important. King Lapis Lazuli, for example, was the twenty-seventh bearer of this title. No other gemstone had more kings taking its name, which gives an idea of the importance of his stone.

For some time, a human king had ruled the land bordering the Dark Forest. He was known to be cruel and power-hungry, treating his people badly according to all reports. This concerned Lapis Lazuli, for he had learned to respect and love many of the humans. They used to attend the happy celebrations in his country, but they had not visited for quite some time. So, the King decided to send emissaries to the land of the humans to inquire whether matters were really as grave as the news made him fear.

This delegation went gladly because the dwarfs all respected their king and took joy in doing as he wished. They never quarreled among each other and lived simply,

content even with the little they had earned from their work. They loved nature and enjoyed themselves most while spending time with the earth, trees and water.

Joyfully, they started their journey one sunny morning, seven little fellows and their ponies. The King himself bade them goodbye and wished them luck. For some time, he stood watching as they waived and finally disappeared into the forest.

That night, Lapis Lazuli had a disturbing dream in which the small troupe was imprisoned by the king of the humans and severely interrogated. Though they were extremely brave and never revealed any secret, they all met their death in the end. Dwarfs pay attention to their dreams, which they believe are sent to proclaim something important. After that, Lapis Lazuli was even more unsettled, fearing the worst.

Week after week went by, but the emissaries did not return. Each day, the people of the dwarfs saw their king wandering atop the palace wall to look for the delegation.

One afternoon, he was again watching over the trees of Dark Forest when the King saw something white approaching from a distance. He called the palace guard, but there seemed to be no danger as they saw only a single

person coming. It appeared that the person was running, and soon the dwarfs recognized the daughter of the goldsmith. They knew her well because she often came with her father to trade for gold.

The girl's name was Chrystalia. The King saw that her long hair was tangled and her arms and legs scratched by the bramble of the forest. Totally out of breath, she reached the palace grounds and broke down. The dwarfs gently picked her up and carried her inside into the protection of the big hall.

After she had regained some strength, Chrystalia tried to explain. "They have captured and imprisoned your emissaries. And, my father has been taken prisoner. Only I was able to flee."

"But why did they do this?" asked the King, most distressed.

"My father's assistant told some of our people that the dwarfs had a stone with the power to grant invisibility. Therefore, they took my father, believing he might know more about this matter."

The King sat in silence. One of the dwarfs must have

29

talked about the secret to the goldsmith's assistant—how foolish!

"What do the humans intend to do?" asked the King.

"I've heard that our king wants to start a war. He needs a significant advantage, however, so he will probably try to steal the stone and its secret," she warned.

The King thanked Chrystalia for her brave help and asked to be left alone. His dream had not misled him. In fact, it had become true.

He got up from his throne and left the hall. Wandering through countless rooms and passages, at last he reached a small spiral staircase. He went up and stood in front of a small chamber that he had never before entered. He was allowed to do so only if the Dark Forest was endangered by the humans. This was certainly the case now.

Slowly he opened the door to the pounding of his heart. A blazing light enveloped him, making it difficult to adjust to its brightness. The King was surprised at how the light filled his heart with joy.

The room, decorated with purple velvet, was equipped with just a small table. On its surface was a velvet cushion, cradling the most wondrous Lapis Lazuli he had ever seen. Nobody could possibly have imagined what the King was feeling right at this moment.

This stone was the one that bestowed on all other gemstones their specific powers. Even though most of the dwarfs knew how to use such powers, they did not know about the whereabouts of their source. This knowledge was meant for the kings alone.

King Lapis Lazuli left the room and closed the door carefully before returning to Crystalia and the other dwarfs. He said to her, "It may be that we will have to leave this area. Do you want to come with us?" She gladly agreed.

When evening came and nothing else had happened, everyone went to sleep except for the guards. The night was as quiet as it was uneventful.

The next morning, however, the guards alarmed the King, saying that a huge army of humans was marching toward Dark Forest. The dwarfs, having no weapons, did not know what to do. They gathered around their ruler and waited for his decision.

The King got up from his throne and spoke only seven words: "The time has come. We will leave."

Then, he went back to the small chamber, where the Lapis Lazuli lay, and entered. For a long time, he looked into the light of the stone, after which he spoke four sentences. Those cannot be repeated here, for they are the secret of the dwarfs.

When the sound of the last letter had faded, the kingdom

of the dwarfs became invisible. Dark Forest ceased to exist—at least to the eyes of the humans. From now on, the dwarfs would live without being detected, able to do their work among the humans in peace.

Very rarely do they ever show themselves today, and then only to pure-hearted humans who have kept their love for the dwarfs. The story of Snow White and the seven dwarfs shows that a little bit of the old times has survived. Even so, most humans regard these stories as mere fairytales. If they only knew!

Excerpt from: Peter Michel, *The Enchanted Aquamarine*, Aquamarin, Grafing, Germany 1985

35

The intelligence of nature discloses to seeking investigators that much in the physical realm receives impetus and development through directing intelligences from the superphysical side of existence. The trees we love, the very sweep of the terrain, the weather we sense, are all acted upon by higher-dimensional minds which work under unchangeable laws to keep the earth inhabited. In fact, all living things in nature are influenced by intelligences whose missions revolve around their physical and inward growth, development and awakenment. In admiration of the forms we behold, we want to remember to salute those God-commissioned beings who dwell on planes invisible to our physical perception. By saluting them and appreciating their ministrations, we shall draw into a closer bond of acquaintanceship with these busy servers.

Go to national parks, not alone to see the outer beauty that they behold, but also to sense the inner presences that guard and permeate these localities. You will gain

much more from your pilgrimages by including a spiritual awareness of the loving minds that make the nature shrines places of peace.

Just as you find a different variety of trees, shrubs or flowers in various areas, so do you come in contact with nature beings whose appearance, emanation and service differ from range to range. Let your inner faculties of intuition and perception identify the invisible powers enveloping the places you visit.

One forest will be vibrant with healing energies which are especially invigorating to the ethereal body. Another mountain fastness will possess a strong current of reverence for God. Lake regions are usually attuned to radiations of peace. The open desert country quickens keenness of mind. These contrasting vibrations are largely due to the types of beings which ensoul the various territories.

Because Mt. Lassen in Northern California is a volcanic site, the nature spirits there are a strange combination of fire and earth beings. Zion National Park contains great stately *Angels of Power*, whereas, not many miles away, Bryce Canyon National Park is inhabited by presences which are particularly gentle and loving. In the out-of-doors we

discover Deva shrines, temples and playgrounds. Zion National Park is a Deva Cathedral radiating waves of spiritual power. Bryce Canyon as well as Yosemite and Yellowstone National Park belong to the Deva playgrounds.

Humanity is the recipient of gracious gifts that come to us hourly through the glories and favors of nature. We are indirectly influenced and enriched but the ministry of those shining presences that are called *Angels of Nature*.

Everywhere we witness the work of this important group of angels, for they keep the earth green, productive and beautiful. The wind, weather and landscape conform to their movements and directions. Even the transition of the seasons is influenced by certain orders who have charge of the quarterly changes.

Fluctuating about us momently are the *Angels of the Elements*. This group has many divisions, for all angelic life evolving through the earth, fire, air and water kingdoms at some period serves nature. The *Angels of Harvest* hover over areas raising food necessary to the human race. The *Angels of the Seasons* each have their own way of vivifying

or making dormant the life they protect. Among the *Weather Angels*, there are two types we should especially respect—they are *Angels of Force*, and *Angels of Calm*. The first group has charge of winds, storms and all manner of turbulent conditions. The second group controls the elements that induce fair, sunny weather.

One day in the mountains, mist rolled past our camp, moistening the whole forest. Soon a high wind started and later everything seemed tumultuous. A heavy storm was brewing. I saw the strange Power Beings who are so dynamic one can scarcely observe them without shuddering. They are God's workers, too, but I think of them with awe, because of the upheavals they often cause.

That night I prayed that the Angels of Calm hover near our camp. Within a few hours, all was peaceful and quiet about us. Yet, the next day we learned at the post office that it had rained during the night in our vicinity. My husband and I exchanged significant glances, and together sent out a prayer of gratitude for the shelter given us.

*Wind Angels* serve in the nature kingdom working with weather conditions to bring productivity to the earth. The

Angels of Force and Angels of Calm serve together to regulate the weather and bring changes to certain areas.

Human beings are permitted to ask for their blessing or protection whenever they require it. A young man was crossing a mountain pass, pulling a house trailer behind his automobile, when the wind became so strong and violent that he feared it would overturn his light car and sent forth a prayer that the Angels of Calm come near to protect him from the gale as he crossed the mountain. No sooner had he opened his eyes, than he noted a lessening in the force of the wind. He continued his journey without further difficulty. His gratitude for this expression of protection from the nature realm was sincere and lasting.

All about us exist the wonders of nature, yet how much wider, deeper and more reverent becomes our appreciation when we admit the inner side of our outer existence. Go to the hills, mountains, canyons, desert or seashore and there you will find intelligent healers and teachers!

Although nature spirits and angels are not directly associated with man, they serve him through their stirring of nature to its rhythmic unfoldment. For this service we are dependent upon nature spirits and we should be filled with gratitude for their manifold ministries. Yet, the chief blessing of realization concerning their inner existence is the inspiration they arouse in us through their selflessness, impersonality, beauty and devotion.

Excerpt from: Flower A. Newhouse, *Rediscovering the Angels*, Escondido 1976

44

# FAIRIES

So many things which matter very much to us do not seem to matter at all to fairies. Life and death, for instance, are things which they know all about; to them there is no uncertainty and no tragedy involved. Mankind so often shrinks from life and fears death. Fairies actually see the flow of life through all things. We live in a world of form without understanding the life force beneath the forms. To us the loss of the form means the end of life, but fairies are never deceived in this way. They have a penetrating and powerful lesson for us.

Why do not most people see fairies? They live in the same world as we do, but their bodies are less dense than ours, though only slightly less dense then a tenuous gas. I feel sure that the veil between us and them is exceedingly thin—so thin that nearly anyone could penetrate it with a little effort along the right line. The difficulty is to indicate this line, and especially to get others to comprehend it.

Excerpt from: Dora van Gelder, *The Real World of Fairies*, Quest Books, Wheaton 1999, pages 2-3

In a little glazed hot-house I found a few fairies of the butterfly variety, longer by an inch or two than others of their type and more human also, but otherwise much the same. Evidently, after a term of hot-house experience, the butterfly type has become specialized for this special contact with the work of man in forcing plants. They are delicate and dainty beings.

There are other kinds of beings which are an integral part of the life of the garden: the trees. In the center of the garden, for instance, there was a large, handsome, free-standing and solitary hickory tree. The aggregation of the vitality of all the living cells in the tree combine to make up the life of an entity which we might call the tree spirit. Thus there is a being who lives, as it were, with the tree as his body, or merging with it. He is an integral part of the tree itself and cannot move about, away from the tree any distance, as the fairies can move among their shrubs. Indeed, there are no trees without tree spirits. This spirit is not always visible, for it only appears when it desires to do so. However, the

consciousness of the tree can project itself externally on occasion and take form. This form, again, usually has a human semblance, but looks much more like an elongated full-size shadow of a human being, very long and very thin. Some of these tree spirits are strong individualities but, of course, the majority are rather undistinguished. This old hickory tree was charming and delightful, and its spirit, whenever it takes form, is rather like a tall brown American Indian shape, rather bark-like skin, high nose, vague hair, and two pin-points of black for eyes. He is not exactly beautiful, but he has great charm, and is exceedingly cheerful and friendly. In some ways, he gives one the feeling of a cheerful, wise old man with quite a whimsical personality.

Dawn is a busy time in the garden, as always at this time of day, a special blessing is poured out upon the world—there is really an awakening of energy, and the fairies are kept busy receiving this and disseminating it. It also begins the activities of their day. At dawn, they come back from play to work once more. The fairies think of the sun as a tremendous life-giving globe of light which is the source of all life, as they derive their nourishment principally from the sun's rays. They seem to draw the

rays of the sun through their bodies: this is the nearest they come to "eating." Apart from deriving energy for the maintenance of their own bodies, they help to guide the energy from the sun for the plants' growth.

Fairies have a delightful relationship with trees, looking upon them as companions who are not so highly evolved as themselves, but have the special merit of being solid, substantial citizen. They like trees and think of them as respectable and worthy and fine, but at the same time they feel rather superior to them because trees cannot move about.

Fairies take a great friendly interest in all animals and in this garden there are some widgeon, ducks and white swans, and they often come down, or look down upon the water from the slope above to watch the antics of these ducks with great delight. There is a close tie with these birds and they often move among them freely, regarding them much as we do dogs, except that they feel slightly more a sense of equality with them. They would always try to help these birds as much as they could, and the birds respond, for like a great many animals, they do see the fairies.

Excerpt from: Dora van Gelder, *The Real World of Fairies*, Quest Books, Wheaton 1999, pages 57-58

# THE CHERRY TREE

When Martha C. Smith was a child in Indiana, she would wander away and sit under a favorite cherry tree in her backyard. There she would see the little people, and sometimes they would even greet her. She watched them by the hour, humming an accompaniment to their songs. Of course, like many other fairy-seers, she was thought odd and accused of daydreaming or even telling fibs.

She never forgot the beautiful, golden fairy-leader, who seemed to command great respect from all her followers. These little ones were about a foot high, dressed in vivid colors and able to come and go in the wink of an eye.

Excerpt from: Marjorie Johnson, *Nature Spirits*, Aquamarin, Grafing, Germany 2000

# THE LITTLE MAN

Ada F. Constable used to live in a small bungalow that stood alone in a field some distance from the village of Walesby, Notinghamshire. One day, her four-year-old son was looking out the window toward the garden, seriously watching something. She said to him, "What are you looking at?" and he replied, "The funny little man." She asked what he was like, and her son gave a fair description of what she associated with a dwarf or gnome wearing a long, pointed cap with the point tapering toward the front. Upon asking what he was doing, she was told with no surprise or excitement, "He's working in the beans, Mummy."

Excerpt from: Marjorie Johnson, *Nature Spirits*, Aquamarin, Grafing, Germany 2000

59

# FAIRY DANCE

As a child, James Alvey from Nottingham lived in the country. A true lover of nature, he frequently would go for long walks across the moor and into the distant hills.

It was on one such walk that he came across a small glade with some flowering harebells, one or two crab-apple trees and several clusters of toadstools. In this clearing, he saw a group of tiny gnome-like men, all very intent on their work as though they had to carry it out quickly. Dumbfounded, he stood watching them for several seconds, after which the men seemed to disappear from view into the surrounding underbrush.

In July 1958, a friend called for James to visit another friend, whose house was in a private, rural setting that had not changed much during the last four hundred years. After getting off the bus, they walked along the road and up the drive to the main door. His friend, who was a little way ahead, entered the house, but he himself felt drawn away from the buildings and further into the surrounding

61

shrubs and trees. He was admiring them when his eyes turned to a laurel bush, around which were dancing at least a dozen pixies and fairies, their faces filled with great happiness.

At this point, he heard the voice of his friend calling, whereupon the little people quickly dispersed, leaving that unforgettable moment imprinted in his mind.

Excerpt from: Marjorie Johnson, *Nature Spirits*, Aquamarin, Grafing, Germany 2000

ordon Harte was once a bus driver in Ireland. One day, in a lonely part of the country, his bus would not start. He had dropped off all his passengers and was quite alone, his conductor having gone to call a mechanic.

While waiting near his bus, he heard faraway voices. Or so he thought until from behind some bushes no further than fifteen feet away came two little men each about two feet tall. One of them told him straightaway that a battery-lead was loose, and he found this to be correct. They talked together about a lot of things, but "it would sound plenty crazy if I told you," Mr. Harte said later.

His conductor shared the next experience with him. They were coming back from a run with the bus in a very lonely place in County Sligo, Eire. As they were rather  early and didn't want to get started before 7 p.m., Mr. Harte was standing waiting beside the cab-door of the bus. Just then, two rabbits dashed out of the bus, and

 immediately after them came the smallest girl he had ever seen—about nine to ten inches tall, He could hardly believe his eyes. When he could finally speak again, he called his conductor from the back of the bus, and he came out and searched the bushes. Then both of them saw her, just for a second, on a small grassy bank twenty-five feet away; but when they got there, she was gone.

When Mr. Harte's grandfather was young, he broke his leg while trying to jump over a river in that part of the country. Up to the time of his death, he claimed that the fairies had helped him from the bank of the river and saved him from drowning. Meanwhile, his wife was "told"—though she could never really say how she knew—that he was in some sort of difficulty, so at 4:30 a.m. she left the house and went to the river, where she found him in great pain. Neighbors helped him get back to his house a half mile away.

"In this part of Ireland, many strange things have happened," said Mr. Harte, "and my mother still tells us some strange stories about the fairies."

Excerpt from: Marjorie Johnson, *Nature Spirits*, Aquamarin, Grafing, Germany 2000

67

# THE LITTLE FAIRY

The wind murmured softly over the dark forests of Moonstone land. Underneath the high ceiling of the branches lived a little bear with a little fairy. They had lived in the forests of Moonstone land from the beginning of time, so long that even they themselves could not remember when they had come to earth.

At first, there were many others like them. The little bears and fairies pledged that they would protect the other animals. For this purpose, the bears of Moonstone land were granted very special abilities. They were able to talk to all other animals and even take their form if necessary. The fairies, however, could already do these things.

The fairies and bears lived a pleasant life and, over time, spread throughout Moonstone land. In spite of this, the little bear, whose name was Lavino, and Lavina, the little fairy, stayed within the forest. Full of joy, they could be seen jumping and dancing everywhere. Their favorite game was to chase each other in the guise of squirrels, leaping through the high branches as the giant trees watched in wonder.

69

The two of them really should not have appeared as squirrels because they were to take on the form of other animals only in cases of emergency. But the angels who watched over Moonstone land thought these little fellows too cute and allowed them to enjoy themselves that way. Those were carefree times, for the animals loved each other and there was no suffering or loss.

Then, one day there was a big commotion. The Bluestar birds that lived at the edges of the forest flew to meet the little fairy and were quite upset. "Big people with colorful hats are approaching. We have heard that they want to take you away to meet their king. But, please, do not leave us!" they begged.

The little fairy had listened attentively and by now was very curious to know what the people with the colorful hats really wanted of her. Not long after that, she could hear their voices.

Meanwhile, the little bear sat on a pile of wood, looking very serious. He feared that the big people would bring only trouble. Soon, five men with huge feather hats came through the trees to greet them.

"Good day, little fairy. We bring greetings from King

Magic Feather. He asks you to come to the realm of the humans. A few days ago, people from another world landed on earth and they need your help. On their home planet, a terrible disease has spread that can be healed only with certain powers available here. But we do not have spaceships and we have no knowledge of how to calculate the route to their world. Nevertheless, our Council of Elders has told us that the fairies know about this. The King is asking you to come and help."

The little fairy listened intensely to the words of the messengers. She asked them for time to think to herself. When the fairy saw the face of the little bear, she knew he did not approve of her going away with the strangers. And, indeed, he insisted that the messengers definitely were lying, though he had no such proof.

But the little fairy did not want to believe the bear. She waived away his warnings as well as those of the other animals of the forest. The story brought by the messengers and the new task at hand sounded very exciting. After all, it was for a good cause. She decided to join the King and help him build spaceships to travel to the faraway planet. The little fairy was sorry to say goodbye to her loved ones, but then she thought about her new task and soon forgot about the others.

After two days of travel, they reached the capital of King Magic Feather's kingdom. Lavina looked intently at everything. There was so much she had never seen before. But there was also so much noise and confusion, and everywhere she encountered horrid smells. She missed the silence of the forest and the lovely fragrance of the moss.

Her reception at the palace was grand. The King explained her responsibilities, which she promised to start right away. First, however, she wanted to talk to the visitors from the other world and decide for herself the meaning of Lavino's warning that the messengers had not spoken true. After a short while, the visitors were led to the palace and they confirmed exactly what the messengers had said. She became totally convinced she was doing the right thing; Lavino must have erred.

Full of energy, she worked day and night calculating mathematical formulas, observing the stars and working on construction papers. Weeks and months went by, and steadily her work progressed. With the construction of the spaceships finally completed, only the calculation of the flight path was yet to be determined.

She was nearly finished when she went to the King to ask one last question. It concerned the problem of the landing. Lavina needed certain schematics to explain the surface conditions of the planet. The King said that she would find what she needed in the old archives. So, leaving her drawings and calculations with him, she went off to visit this secluded place.

When she asked the custodian who worked there for help, he began to consult a huge index. He then directed the little fairy to the archive's lowest chambers, which were deep down below the earth's surface. He also explained that nobody had worked there for a very long time.

Lavina went into the depths and looked through the papers on the dusty shelves. Af-ter a while, she found the information she needed and was just about to climb up the stairs when she heard a faint knocking. But there was no door anywhere to be seen. Realizing that the sound was coming from the back of the room, she called out. She heard a distant answer even though she couldn't understand the words. Searching around, she accidentally touched one of the shelves and somehow triggered it to open into a dark chamber. Much to her surprise, an old man with a walking stick came out.

"Who are you and why are you living beneath the earth?" she gasped. Lavina couldn't help be astonished.

"This is a long story," said the old man slowly. "But, I will tell you. For many years, I was the astronomer of the King. One day a spaceship landed here with people from another planet. They had been expelled from their world because of violating their laws. They told our King about the immense treasures of their world and convinced him to equip an army to conquer their planet. They were from a place inhabited by beings with no weapons, and so it seemed easy for him to succeed."

"Our King asked me to build spaceships and to calculate the course to their planet. When he told me his plan to overtake their planet, I refused and was taken prisoner. He said he would find somebody else to finish the job. Therefore, I am sitting here, waiting for my fate to be delivered."

When Lavina heard those words, she began to cry. Yes, they had lied to her. She had been awfully misused. In fact, she had worked out plans that might well cost the lives of an entire people. She must prevent this from happening, of course.

Determined, she ran back to the palace. The King immediately realized what had happened. He gave orders to have Lavina thrown into the archive prison, where she would be kept along with the old astronomer. Full of regret and sorrow, she silently wept, not knowing how to undo what she had created.

Some time later, the door opened and the two prisoners were taken before the King. Pointing to an area filled with countless spaceships, he declared. "You should at least be allowed to watch your work unfold. I thank you and will leave now. You are free to go wherever you like."

Consumed by her sadness and remorse, the little fairy left town while the spaceships roamed the sky. However, she never found out what really happened—the ships crashed on the distant planet, to be destroyed during landing.

On her way back to the forest, Lavina thought only about the little bear and the animals of Moonstone land. Was Lavino waiting for her to return? Experience tells us that bears are very faithful. But who knows?

Excerpt from: Peter Michel, *The Enchanted Aquamarine*, Aquamarin, Grafing, Germany 1985

# ILLUSTRATIONS

For the complete texts by Flower A. Newhouse,
please contact:
The Christward Ministry
20560 Questhaven Road
Escondido, California 92025


For the complete texts by Dora van Gelder-Kunz,
please contact:
The Theosophical Publishing House
P.O.Box
Wheaton, Illinois 60189-0270